UNCANNY X-FORCE

SAM HUMPHRIES
WRITER

········· **ISSUES #1-4** ·········

PENCILER RON GARNEY **INKERS** DANNY MIKI (#1-2) & SCOTT HANNA (#2-4)

COLORISTS MARTE GRACIA WITH ISRAEL GONZALEZ & WIL QUINTANA

MINDSCAPE PAGES ADRIAN ALPHONA & CHRISTINA STRAIN

········· **ISSUES #5-6** ·········

ARTISTS ADRIAN ALPHONA & DEXTER SOY

COLORISTS CHRISTINA STRAIN, DAVID CURIEL & CHRIS SOTOMAYOR

LETTERER VC'S CORY PETIT

COVER ART OLIVIER COIPEL & LAURA MARTIN (#1), KRIS ANKA (#2-5) AND MARCOS MARTIN (#6)

ASSOCIATE EDITOR JORDAN D. WHITE **EDITOR** NICK LOWE

SPECIAL THANKS TO STEVEN CHISM, DANIEL HENRIQUES & ALLEN MARTINEZ

COLLECTION EDITOR: **JENNIFER GRÜNWALD** • ASSISTANT EDITORS: **ALEX STARBUCK** & **NELSON RIBEIRO** • EDITOR, SPECIAL PROJECTS: **MARK D. BEAZLEY**
SENIOR EDITOR, SPECIAL PROJECTS: **JEFF YOUNGQUIST** • SVP OF PRINT & DIGITAL PUBLISHING SALES: **DAVID GABRIEL** • BOOK DESIGN: **JEFF POWELL**
EDITOR IN CHIEF: **AXEL ALONSO** • CHIEF CREATIVE OFFICER: **JOE QUESADA** • PUBLISHER: **DAN BUCKLEY** • EXECUTIVE PRODUCER: **ALAN FINE**

LET IT BLEED

PSYLOCKE?!

"SPI

GET AWAY FROM ME!

"--WHAT DID YOU FIND IN THIS *EMAIL?*"

DEAR CUTLERY KID--

AND--I WILL GIVE YOU THIS--YOU WERE RIGHT.

ALTHOUGH I AM ENJOYING THE LOCAL WILDLIFE.

THERE'S SOMETHING WEIRD GOING ON, A NEW CULT, OR A NEW DRUG, OR MIND CONTROL, OR ALL OF THE ABOVE.

CURSE YOU FOR SENDING ME HERE. IT'S WINTER, BUT THERE'S NO SNOW ON THE GROUND.

THE DRUG IS CALLED TAO, OR MAYBE IT'S AN ACRONYM FOR "TOGETHER AS ONE."

THEY SAY IT MAKES YOU FEEL "TOGETHER," LIKE YOU BELONG, A SENSE OF UNITY.

THE BAD NEWS IS IT MAKES YOU SUSCEPTIBLE TO SOME SORT OF HIVE MIND MENTALITY.

(IT ALSO SEEMS TO MAKE YOU DANCE LIKE A COMPLETE JACKASS.)

AND THE ONE WHO CONTROLS TAO, THE ONE WHO CALLS THE SHOTS-- IT'S THE ONE YOU WERE AFRAID OF.

SEND BACKUP.

SORRY TO HAVE MISSED BOXING DAY DEBAUCHERY AT THE CABIN. YOU BETTER HAVE SAVED ME A BEER AND A TURKEY LEG.

SIGNED, YOUR SASKATCHEWAN SWEETIE

THIS PLACE IS PACKED. WE STAY *OUT OF SIGHT* UNTIL EVERYONE *LEAVES.* THEN WE *INVESTIGATE.*

TO SAY THAT BETSY AND [...] HAD *UNFINISHED* BUSINESS [...] BE AN *UNDERSTATEMENT.*

BETSY *NO!!*

WAIT[...]

LEAVE ME ALONE!

NEVER.

BETSY'S SWORD, THE *SHURAYUKI,* WAS FORGED IN JAPAN A THOUSAND YEARS AGO. IT WAS GIVEN TO HER BY AN OLD FRIEND.

THE *SHURAYUKI* HAS THIRSTED FOR SPIRAL'S BLOOD FOR SOME TIME.

THIS IS IT!

I DON'T SUPPOSE YOU'VE PICKED UP ANY *SUPER-STRENGTH?*

HURK--

GUH GUH GUH

FINALLY. I MADE IT. I'M BACK.

I'M BAAACK!

LUCAS BISHOP BETRAYED HIS FRIENDS AND WAS ABANDONED THOUSANDS OF YEARS IN THE FUTURE. IT WAS NOT A FORGIVING PLACE.

HE HAS NOT BEEN THE SAME SINCE.

GIMME SHELTER

STOP HER!

LEAVE US ALONE!

THERE'S NO NEED TO BE *SCARED*, CHILD!

PUCK, CAN YOU--?

DO I *LOOK* LIKE I'M GOOD WITH KIDS?

AR

BACK OFF, STORM!

SPIRAL!

STEP *AWAY* FROM THE GIRL!

WHERE'D *SHE* COME FROM?

YOU MAKE ME *LAUGH*, STORM.

IN THIS WORLD, WHAT'S A *GODDESS* GOT ON A *NINJA?*

PUCK! SHE'S A *TELEPORTER!* IF SHE PUTS HER *ARMS* TOGETHER--!

I'M ON IT!

VZZOM

"YOU INTOXICATE ME, CLUSTER.

SZÉCHENYI CHAIN BRIDGE OVER THE RIVER DANUBE BUDAPEST, HUNGARY

"I WANTED TO SHOW THE MOST BEAUTIFUL CITY IN THE WORLD TO THE MOST BEAUTIFUL WOMAN IN THE WORLD.

"AND I ONLY HAD TO HIJACK ONE SHIP TO DO IT."

"NOW THAT E.V.A. IS AT THE CONTROLS, AND OUR MAIN COURSE OF SEARED FOIE GRAS WITH SOUP DUMPLINGS IS FINISHED--I HAVE SOMETHING FOR YOU."

I KNOW IT'S NOT VALENTINE'S DAY YET, BUT-- HERE.

A SMALL TOKEN OF MY HEART'S PASSION. FOR YOU, CLUSTER.

OH FANTOMEX, YOU--

YOU GOT ME--

TOOTHBRUSHES

WHERE IS IT, WHERE IS IT--?

HERE IT IS! HAD TO LEAVE THE *OTHER* ONE AT THE CLUB...

THERE. NOW YOU'RE *HIDDEN* AGAIN.

I DON'T KNOW HOW THEY *FOUND* US. I THOUGHT I WAS *CAREFUL*, I THOUGHT THAT PLACE WAS *SHIELDED*.

BUT WE'RE *HOME* NOW, EVERYTHING IS *OKAY*. YOU'VE GOT YOUR *BRACELET* BACK, NO ONE CAN *FIND* US.

NOT *CYCLOPS* AND HIS *XAVIER KILL CREW*, NOT *WOLVERINE* AND HIS *BRAINWASH SCHOOL*--

AND *DEFINITELY* NOT THAT *PURPLE HAIRED*--

WRONG.

SWEET VIRGINIA

WHERE DID HE GO?

IT'S TOO *DAMN* DARK--

I COULD NOT HAVE *MISSED*, HE WAS RIGHT IN *FRONT* OF--

PUCK!

TH UNK

GRAAAH

HAI!

KAAAUGH

STREET FIGHTING MAN

VZZOM

BISHOP! YOUR SKULL IS MINE!

RAAAGH!

KRA-KOOM

THERE. I'D RECOGNIZE THAT BRAND OF CHAOS ANYWHERE.

BETSY'S CLOSE.

FANTOMEX, THAT WOMAN WITH ALL THE ARMS IS A NINJA LIKE OUR BETSY. SHOULD WE GET INVOLVED?

GREETINGS.

WE'RE CLOSED.

I WAS HOPING YOU COULD MAKE AN EXCEPTION.

ONE GIBSON MARTINI, PLEASE. VERY COLD, VERY DRY, VERY DIRTY.

I HAVE BEEN CRAVING ONE FOR A LONG TIME.

BEFORE HE WAS TRAPPED IN THE FUTURE, BISHOP WENT ROGUE. HE WAS CONVINCED THAT HOPE, THE FIRST NEW MUTANT IN YEARS, WOULD TRIGGER AN APOCALYPTIC FUTURE.

BISHOP RATIONALIZED THAT HE MUST KILL HER. HE WAS RELENTLESS, UNSTOPPABLE-- DEDICATED TO MURDERING A CHILD, NO MATTER WHO GOT IN THE WAY.

IN THE [LABY]RINTH, [M]EMORY [BI]SHOP'S [RE]ALITY AND [COMM]ITMENT [LOC]KED AND [SNA]RED [HI]M.

[SH]E WAS STILL [A]NGRY THAT [BI]SHOP'S [O]BSESSION [TO]OK HIM [A]WAY FROM [TH]E X-MEN, [FR]OM HER.

KRZZACT

SO IN THE MOMENT, STORM RATIONALIZED: TO GET HER FRIEND BACK, SHE MUST KILL THAT MEMORY.

[S]TORM!

WHERE ARE YOU-- HUH?

ORORO! I THOUGHT I LOST YOU!

I AM ALL RIGHT, BETSY. LET'S CONTINUE ON AND GET [OUT OF THIS]

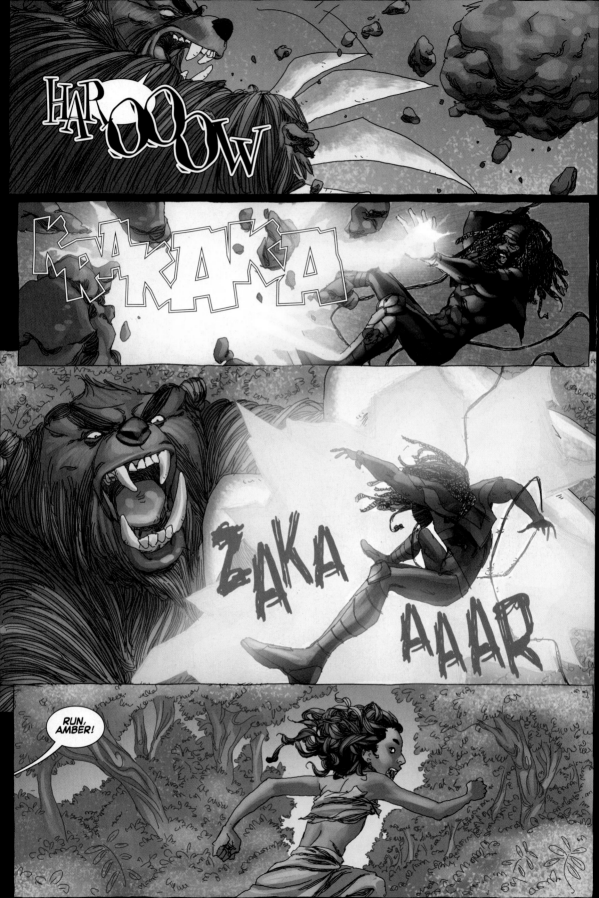

UNCANNY X FORCE

6

WILD HORSES

KLAK

HOW *DARE* YOU *ABDUCT* ME LIKE I'M SOME COMMON--

ELIZABETH, LISTEN!

IT'S *FANTOMEX!* WEAPON XIII *CAPTURED* HIM!

PLEASE-- I KNOW WHAT HE DID TO YOU, BUT YOU MUST HELP ME *SAVE* FANTOMEX!

...FANTOMEX IS WHAT?

CLUSTER-- AFTER *EVERYTHING* THAT'S *HAPPENED*-- *HOW* CAN YOU ASK ME THAT?

THE ANSWER IS *NO.*

VZZOM

WHAT HAPPENED AFTER *THAT?*

SHH, QUIET!

YOU HEAR THAT *NOISE?*

NO, I DON'T.

FINE. YOU DON'T HAVE TO SAY WHAT HAPPENED NEXT.

LOGAN. WHEN YOU SENT ME AFTER *SPIRAL...*

...DID YOU *EXPECT* ME TO *KILL* FOR YOU?

WELL...

THERE'S A LOT OF *BAD BLOOD* THERE, AND...

I DIDN'T KNOW *WHAT* YOU WOULD DO.

YOU'RE FULL OF ▮▮▮.

READ MY MIND IF YOU DON'T BELIEVE ME.

WHAT A GREAT EXAMPLE YOU SET FOR YOUR STUDENTS.

YOU GIVE UP DIRTY WORK AND MANIPULATE YOUR FRIENDS INTO DOING IT FOR YOU.

WE'RE SUPPOSED TO TRUST EACH OTHER!

I DON'T KNOW WHO YOU ARE ANYMORE!

I'M PUTTING MY NECK ON THE LINE FOR OUR FUTURE. AND YOU WANNA JUST ▮▮▮ AROUND IN LOS ANGELES AND SCREW IT UP FOR THE REST OF US!

NOT ALL OF US ARE GOING TO GO WITH YOU OR CYCLOPS. WE'RE NOT ALL THAT CONVENIENT.

YOU MARGINALIZE THE MUTANTS THAT DON'T FIT INTO YOUR SIMPLE WORLDVIEW. AND THAT'S WHEN THEY GET ISOLATED. AND DESPERATE.

LIKE SPIRAL.

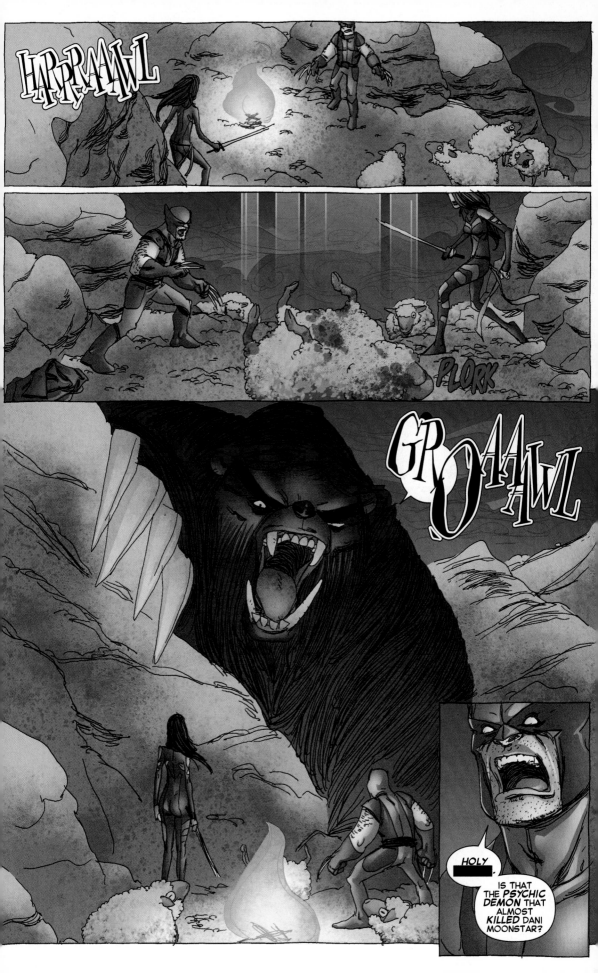

SHHH. EASY NOW.

WOLVERINE, MEET *DEMON BEAR*. STORM AND I FOUND HIM *DESTROYING* BISHOP'S PSYCHE.

I PULLED A FIGURATIVE *THORN* FROM HIS METAPHYSICAL *PAW*. AS A RESULT, HE'S BECOME QUITE *ATTACHED* TO ME.

HURFF

WHEN WE ESCAPED BISHOP'S PSYCHE, HE *STOWED AWAY* WITH ME, HIDING DEEP IN MY *MIND*. THOUGHT HE'D *NEVER* COME OUT.

THAT'S WHAT I'VE BEEN DOING WITH THE *SHEEP*. I'VE BEEN *LURING* HIM OUT... *HUNTING* HIM.

I'M *NOT* COMING BACK TO THE SCHOOL, WOLVERINE. THAT'S *YOUR* HOME, NOT *MINE*.

I'M NEITHER THE *HERD* NOR THE *SHEPHERD*. I'M SOMETHING *ELSE*, ENTIRELY.

DEAL WITH IT.

THIS AIN'T *OVER*, PSYLOCKE. JUST CUZ *DEMON BEAR* SHOWED UP TO SAVE YOUR ASS--

YOU'RE *WRONG*, WOLVERINE. THE DEMON BEAR SAVED *YOU*.

GOODBYE.

=BIP=

HURFF

NEXT:
ONE-WAY TICKET
TO MADRIPOOR!

UNCANNY X-FORCE #1 VARIANT
BY SKOTTIE YOUNG

UNCANNY X-FORCE #1 VARIANT
BY RON GARNEY & MARTE GRACIA

UNCANNY X-FORCE #2 VARIANT
BY ED McGUINNESS & MORRY HOLLOWELL

UNCANNY X-FORCE #3 VARIANT
BY SALVADOR LARROCA & FRANK D'ARMATA

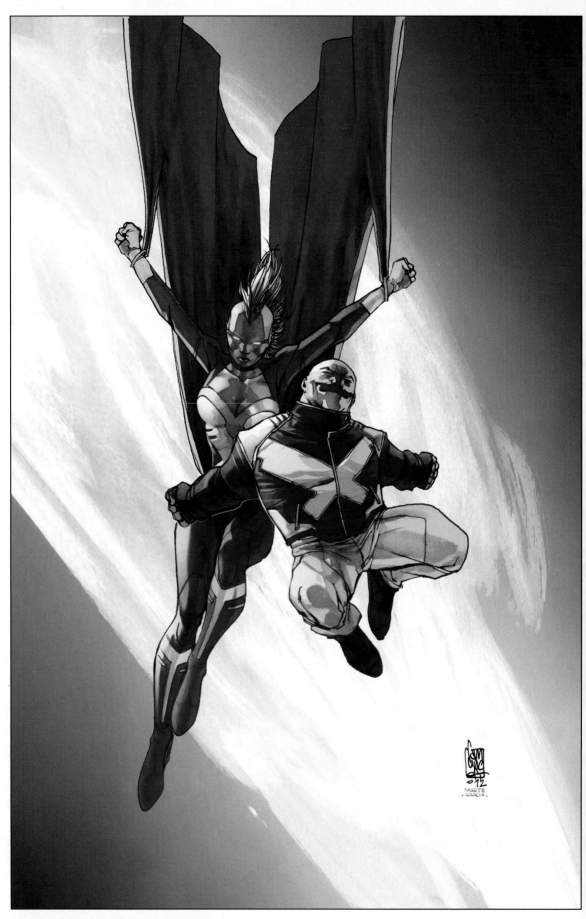

UNCANNY X-FORCE #4 VARIANT
BY GIUSEPPE CAMUNCOLI & MARTE GRACIA

UNCANNY X-FORCE #5 VARIANT
BY MILO MANARA

UNCANNY X-FORCE #1
DESIGN VARIANT
BY KRIS ANKA

UNCANNY X-FORCE #6
WOLVERINE COSTUME VARIANT
BY CARLOS PAGULAYAN & CHRIS SOTOMAYOR

TO ACCESS THE FREE *MARVEL AUGMENTED REALITY APP* THAT ENHANCES AND CHANGES THE WAY YOU EXPERIENCE COMICS:

1. Download the app for free via marvel.com/ARapp
2. Launch the app on your camera-enabled Apple iOS® or Android™ device*
3. Hold your mobile device's camera over any cover or panel with the **AR** graphic.
4. Sit back and see the future of comics in action!

*Available on most camera-enabled Apple iOS® and Android™ devices. Content subject to change and availability.

AR

INDEX

Issue #1
Sam Humphries welcomes you to *Uncanny X-Force* .... Page 1, Panel 1
Senior Editor Nick Lowe on Bishop.. Page 20, Panel 1

Issue #2
Nick Lowe on Spiral .... Page 4, Panel 2
Sam Humphries on Bishop .... Page 20, Panel 1

Issue #3
Sam Humphries on Ron Garney .... Page 1, Panel 5

Issue #4
Art evolution.. Page 2, Panel 3
Sam Humphries on choosing the Uncanny X-Force team... Page 9, Panel 4

Issue #5
Bishop board game commercial .... Page 4, Panel 1
Demon Bear Humane Society .... Page 16, Panel 3

Issue #6
"Thoughts" of the sheep in Psylocke's psychic herd.. Page 1, Panel 4
Editorial Confessions: What would your psychic dreamscape look like?......................... Page 2, Panel 3